Costumes for
Lilac
Professional Champion

layback
spin

Costumes for
Sunya

sit spin

Costumes for
Kirk

spread
eagle

camel spin

death
spiral

Costumes for
Tiffany & Charley

cut out

Salchow

Russian split

Costumes for
Irina & Oleg

Axel

Medal Ceremony

Sunya

Kirk

Lutz

Pairs Champions

Tiffany
&
Charley